SHORT FORM of Contract

PARTICULAR CONDITIONS

RULES FOR ADJUDICATION

First Edition 1999
ISBN 2-88432-024-5

NOTES FOR GUIDANCE

FEDERATION INTERNATIONALE DES INGENIEURS-CONSEILS
INTERNATIONAL FEDERATION OF CONSULTING ENGINEERS
INTERNATIONALE VEREINIGUNG BERATENDER INGENIEURE
FEDERACION INTERNACIONAL DE INGENIEROS CONSULTORES

ACKNOWLEDGEMENTS

The Fédération Internationale des Ingénieurs-Conseils (FIDIC) extends special thanks to the following members of its Task Group: Philip Jenkinson (Task Group Leader), WS Atkins, UK; AEJ (Tony) Sanders, Mouchel, UK; and Edward Corbett, Corbett & Co, UK. Liaison with other active Task Groups was provided by Peter L Booen, GIBB Ltd, UK.

The preparation was carried out under the general direction of the FIDIC Contracts Committee comprising John B Bowcock (Chairman), Consulting Engineer, UK; Michael Mortimer-Hawkins, SwedPower, Sweden; Axel-Volkmar Jaeger, Schmidt Reuter Partner, Germany; and KB (Tony) Norris (Special Adviser), Consulting Engineer, UK.

Drafts were commented on by the following persons and organisations: Mushtaq Ahmad, NESPAK, Pakistan; Peter Batty, Post Buckley International, USA; Nael G Bunni, Consulting Engineer, Ireland; Kathryn Josephine T. dela Cruz, Construction Industry Authority of the Philippines; Michael Dudley, UNOPS; Hans Enhörning, ABB Asea Brown Boveri Ltd, Switzerland; Mark Griffiths, Griffiths & Armour, UK; Geoffrey F Hawker, Consulting Engineer and Barrister, UK; Adam K Heine, Consulting Engineer, Poland; HS Kwong, Secretary for Works, Hong Kong; Jan Cees Overbosch/Evert Jan Wijers, DHV Beheer BV, The Netherlands; Marek Rdultowski, Cosmopoli Consultants, Poland; J G Rees, Binnie Black & Veatch, UK; Asian Development Bank; European Bank for Reconstruction and Development; Inter-American Development Bank; International Association of Dredging Companies; Inter-Pacific Bar Association; ORGAnisme de Liaison Industries Métalliques Européennes ("ORGALIME"); and The World Bank. Acknowledgement of reviewers does not mean that such persons or organizations approve the wording of all clauses.

FIDIC wishes to record its appreciation of the time and effort devoted by all the above.

The ultimate decision on the form and content of the document rests with FIDIC.

FOREWORD

These Conditions of Contract have been prepared by the Fédération Internationale des Ingénieurs-Conseils (FIDIC) and are recommended for engineering and building work of relatively small capital value. However, depending on the type of work and the circumstances, the Conditions may be suitable for contracts of greater value. They are considered most likely to be suitable for fairly simple or repetitive work or work of short duration without the need for specialist sub-contracts.

The main aim has been to produce a straightforward flexible document which includes all essential commercial provisions and which may be used for all types of engineering and building work with a variety of administrative arrangements. Under the usual arrangements for this type of contract, the Contractor constructs the Works in accordance with design provided by the Employer or by his representative (if any). However, this form may also be suitable for contracts which include, or wholly comprise, contractor-designed civil, mechanical and/or electrical works.

In addition, the Employer has a choice of valuation methods. Furthermore, although there is no reference to an impartial Engineer, the Employer may appoint an independent Engineer to act impartially, should he wish to do so.

The form is recommended for general use, though modifications may be required in some jurisdictions. FIDIC considers the official and authentic text to be the version in the English language.

The intention is that all necessary information should be provided in the Appendix to the Agreement, the latter incorporating the tenderer's offer and its acceptance in one simple document. The General Conditions are expected to cover the majority of contracts. Nevertheless, users will be able to introduce Particular Conditions if they wish, to cater for special cases or circumstances. The General Conditions and the Particular Conditions will together comprise the Conditions governing the rights and obligations of the parties.

To assist in the preparation of tender documents using these Conditions, Notes for Guidance are included. These Notes will not become one of the documents forming the Contract. Finally, applicable Rules for Adjudication are also included.

The attention of users is drawn to the FIDIC publication "Tendering Procedure", which presents a systematic approach to the selection of tenderers and the obtaining and evaluation of tenders.

CONTENTS

Particular Conditions

Rules for Adjudication

Notes for Guidance

SHORT FORM of Contract

Agreement

First Edition 1999

FEDERATION INTERNATIONALE DES INGENIEURS-CONSEILS
INTERNATIONAL FEDERATION OF CONSULTING ENGINEERS
INTERNATIONALE VEREINIGUNG BERATENDER INGENIEURE
FEDERACION INTERNACIONAL DE INGENIEROS CONSULTORES

FIDIC

Agreement

The Employer is _____ of

_____

The Contractor is _____ of

_____

The Employer desires the execution of certain Works known as _____

_____

OFFER

The Contractor has examined the documents listed in the Appendix which forms part of this Agreement and offers to execute the Works in conformity with the Contract for the sum of

_____ (in words)

_____ (in figures) (_____)

or such other sum as may be ascertained under the Contract.

This offer, of which the Contractor has submitted two signed originals, may be accepted by the Employer by signing and returning one original of this document to the Contractor before

_____ (date)

The Contractor understands that the Employer is not bound to accept the lowest or any offer received for the Works.

Signature: _____ Date: _____

Name: _____ Authorised to sign on behalf of (*organization name*): _____

Capacity: _____ _____

ACCEPTANCE

The Employer has by signing below, accepted the Contractor's offer and agrees that in consideration for the execution of the Works by the Contractor, the Employer shall pay the Contractor in accordance with the Contract. This Agreement comes into effect on the date when the Contractor receives one original of this document signed by the Employer.

Signature: _____ Date: _____

Name: _____ Authorised to sign on behalf of (*organization name*): _____

Capacity: _____ _____

AGREEMENT

GENERAL
CONDITIONS

RULES FOR
ADJUDICATION

GUIDANCE

APPENDIX

This Appendix forms part of the Agreement.

[Note: with the exception of the items for which the Employer's requirements have been inserted, the Contractor shall complete the following information before submitting his offer.]

Item	Sub-Clause	Data
Documents forming the Contract listed in the order of priority	1.1.1	

Document (delete if not applicable)		Document Identification
(a) The Agreement		
(b) Particular Conditions		
(c) General Conditions		
(d) The Specification		
(e) The Drawings		
(f) The Contractor's tendered design		
(g) The bill of quantities		
(h)		
(i)		

Item	Sub-Clause	Data
Time for Completion	1.1.9	_____ days
Law of the Contract	1.4	Law of the Country* ___
Language	1.5	
Provision of Site	2.1	On the Commencement Date* ___
Authorised person	3.1	
Name and address of Employer's representative (if known)	3.2	
Performance security (if any):		
Amount	4.4	
Form	4.4	(details)

Employer to amend as appropriate

Item	Sub-Clause	Data
Requirements for Contractor's design (if any)	5.1	Specification Clause No's _____ _____
Programme:		
Time for submission	7.2	Within 14 days* of the Commencement Date.
Form of programme	7.2	_____ _____
Amount payable due to failure to complete	7.4	_____ per day up to a maximum of 10%* of sum stated in the Agreement
Period for notifying defects	9.1 & 11.5	365 days* calculated from the date stated in the notice under Sub-Clause 8.2
Variation procedure		
Daywork rates	10.2	_____ _____ _____ (details)
Valuation of the Works*		
Lump sum Price	11.1	_____ (details)
Lump sum price with schedules of rates	11.1	_____ (details)
Lump sum price with bill of quantities	11.1	_____ (details)
Remeasurement with tender bill of quantities	11.1	_____ (details)
Cost reimbursable	11.1	_____ (details)
Percentage of value of Materials and Plant	11.2	Materials _____ 80%*
		Plant _____ 90%*

Employer to amend as appropriate

Item	Sub-Clause	Data
Percentage of retention	11.3	5%
Currency of payment	11.7	
Rate of interest	11.8	_____ % per annum
Insurances	14.1	

Type of cover*	Amount of cover*	Exclusions*
The Works, Materials, Plant and fees	The sum stated in the Agreement plus 15%	
Contractor's Equipment	Full replacement cost	
Third Party injury to persons and damage to property		
Workers		
Other cover*		

Arbitration

Rules	15.3	UNCITRAL Arbitration Rules* _____ (details)
Appointing authority	15.3	President of FIDIC or his nominee* _____ (details)
Place of Arbitration	15.3	The Country* _____

*Employer to amend as appropriate

SHORT FORM of Contract

General Conditions

First Edition 1999

FEDERATION INTERNATIONALE DES INGENIEURS-CONSEILS
INTERNATIONAL FEDERATION OF CONSULTING ENGINEERS
INTERNATIONALE VEREINIGUNG BERATENDER INGENIEURE
FEDERACION INTERNACIONAL DE INGENIEROS CONSULTORES

General Conditions

1 General Provisions

**1.1
Definitions**

In the Contract as defined below, the words and expressions defined shall have the following meanings assigned to them, except where the context requires otherwise:

The Contract

1.1.1   "**Contract**" means the Agreement and the other documents listed in the Appendix.

1.1.2   "**Specification**" means the document as listed in the Appendix, including Employer's requirements in respect of design to be carried out by the Contractor, if any, and any Variation to such document.

1.1.3   "**Drawings**" means the Employer's drawings of the Works as listed in the Appendix, and any Variation to such drawings.

Persons

1.1.4   "**Employer**" means the person named in the Agreement and the legal successors in title to this person, but not (except with the consent of the Contractor) any assignee.

1.1.5   "**Contractor**" means the person named in the Agreement and the legal successors in title to this person, but not (except with the consent of the Employer) any assignee.

1.1.6   "**Party**" means either the Employer or the Contractor.

Dates, Times and Periods

1.1.7   "**Commencement Date**" means the date 14 days after the date the Agreement comes into effect or any other date agreed between the Parties.

1.1.8   "**day**" means a calendar day.

1.1.9   "**Time for Completion**" means the time for completing the Works as stated in the Appendix (or as extended under Sub-Clause 7.3), calculated from the Commencement Date.

Money and Payments

1.1.10   "**Cost**" means all expenditure properly incurred (or to be incurred) by the Contractor, whether on or off the Site, including overheads and similar charges, but does not include profit.

Other Definitions

1.1.11   "**Contractor's Equipment**" means all apparatus, machinery, vehicles, facilities and other things required for the execution of the Works but does not include Materials or Plant.

1.1.12   "**Country**" means the country in which the Site is located.

1.1.13   "**Employer's Liabilities**" means those matters listed in Sub-Clause 6.1.

1.1.14   "**Force Majeure**" means an exceptional event or circumstance: which is beyond a Party's control; which such Party could not reasonably have provided against before entering into the Contract; which, having arisen, such Party could not reasonably have avoided or overcome; and, which is not substantially attributable to the other Party.

1.1.15   "Materials" means things of all kinds (other than Plant) intended to form or forming part of the permanent work.

1.1.16   "Plant" means the machinery and apparatus intended to form or forming part of the permanent work.

1.1.17   "Site" means the places provided by the Employer where the Works are to be executed, and any other places specified in the Contract as forming part of the Site.

1.1.18   "Variation" means a change to the Specification and /or Drawings (if any) which is instructed by the Employer under Sub-Clause 10.1.

1.1.19   "Works" means all the work and design (if any) to be performed by the Contractor including temporary work and any Variation

1.2

Interpretation

Words importing persons or parties shall include firms and organisations. Words importing singular or one gender shall include plural or the other gender where the context requires.

1.3

Priority of Documents

The documents forming the Contract are to be taken as mutually explanatory of one another. If an ambiguity or discrepancy is found in the documents, the Employer shall issue any necessary instructions to the Contractor, and the priority of the documents shall be in accordance with the order as listed in the Appendix.

1.4

Law

The law of the Contract is stated in the Appendix.

1.5

Communications

Wherever provision is made for the giving or issue of any notice, instruction, or other communication by any person, unless otherwise specified such communication shall be written in the language stated in the Appendix and shall not be unreasonably withheld or delayed.

1.6

Statutory Obligations

The Contractor shall comply with the laws of the countries where activities are performed. The Contractor shall give all notices and pay all fees and other charges in respect of the Works.

The 2 Employer

2.1
Provision of Site

The Employer shall provide the Site and right of access thereto at the times stated in the Appendix.

2.2

Permits and Licences

The Employer shall, if requested by the Contractor, assist him in applying for permits, licences or approvals which are required for the Works.

AGREEMENT

GENERAL
CONDITIONS

RULES FOR
ADJUDICATION

GUIDANCE

| 2.3 Employer's Instructions | The Contractor shall comply with all instructions given by the Employer in respect of the Works including the suspension of all or part of the Works. |

| 2.4 Approvals | No approval or consent or absence of comment by the Employer or the Employer's representative shall affect the Contractor's obligations. |

3 Employer's Representatives

| 3.1 Authorised Person | One of the Employer's personnel shall have authority to act for him. This authorised person shall be as stated in the Appendix, or as otherwise notified by the Employer to the Contractor. |

| 3.2 Employer's Representative | The Employer may also appoint a firm or individual to carry out certain duties. The appointee may be named in the Appendix, or notified by the Employer to the Contractor from time to time. The Employer shall notify the Contractor of the delegated duties and authority of this Employer's representative. |

4 The Contractor

| 4.1 General Obligations | The Contractor shall carry out the Works properly and in accordance with the Contract. The Contractor shall provide all supervision, labour, Materials, Plant and Contractor's Equipment which may be required. All Materials and Plant on Site shall be deemed to be the property of the Employer. |

| 4.2 Contractor's Representative | The Contractor shall submit to the Employer for consent the name and particulars of the person authorised to receive instructions on behalf of the Contractor. |

| 4.3 Subcontracting | The Contractor shall not subcontract the whole of the Works. The Contractor shall not subcontract any part of the Works without the consent of the Employer. |

| 4.4 Performance Security | If stated in the Appendix, the Contractor shall deliver to the Employer within 14 days of the Commencement Date a performance security in a form and from a third party approved by the Employer. |

5 Design by Contractor

| 5.1 Contractor's Design | The Contractor shall carry out design to the extent specified, as referred to in the Appendix. The Contractor shall promptly submit to the Employer all designs prepared by him. Within 14 days of receipt the Employer shall notify any comments or, if the design submitted is not in accordance with the Contract, shall reject it stating the reasons. The Contractor shall not construct any element of the permanent work designed by him within 14 days after the design has been |

submitted to the Employer or where the design for that element has been rejected. Design that has been rejected shall be promptly amended and resubmitted. The Contractor shall resubmit all designs commented on taking these comments into account as necessary.

5.2

Responsibility for Design

The Contractor shall remain responsible for his tendered design and the design under this Clause, both of which shall be fit for the intended purposes defined in the Contract and he shall also remain responsible for any infringement of any patent or copyright in respect of the same. The Employer shall be responsible for the Specification and Drawings.

6 Employer's Liabilities

6.1

Employer's Liabilities

In this Contract, Employer's Liabilities mean :

a) war, hostilities (whether war be declared or not), invasion, act of foreign enemies, within the Country,

b) rebellion, terrorism, revolution, insurrection, military or usurped power, or civil war, within the Country,

c) riot, commotion or disorder by persons other than the Contractor's personnel and other employees, affecting the Site and/or the Works,

d) ionising radiations, or contamination by radio-activity from any nuclear fuel, or from any nuclear waste from the combustion of nuclear fuel, radio-active toxic explosive, or other hazardous properties of any explosive nuclear assembly or nuclear component of such an assembly, except to the extent to which the Contractor may be responsible for the use of any radio-active material,

e) pressure waves caused by aircraft or other aerial devices travelling at sonic or supersonic speeds,

f) use or occupation by the Employer of any part of the Works, except as may be specified in the Contract,

g) design of any part of the Works by the Employer's personnel or by others for whom the Employer is responsible, and

h) any operation of the forces of nature affecting the Site and/or the Works, which was unforeseeable or against which an experienced contractor could not reasonably have been expected to take precautions.

i) Force Majeure,

j) a suspension under Sub-Clause 2.3 unless it is attributable to the Contractor's failure,

k) any failure of the Employer,

l) physical obstructions or physical conditions other than climatic conditions, encountered on the Site during the performance of the Works, which obstructions or conditions were not reasonably foreseeable by an experienced contractor and which the Contractor immediately notified to the Employer,

m) any delay or disruption caused by any Variation,

n) any change to the law of the Contract after the date of the Contractor's offer as stated in the Agreement,

o) losses arising out of the Employer's right to have the permanent work executed on, over, under, in or through any land, and to occupy this land for the permanent work, and

p) damage which is an unavoidable result of the Contractor's obligations to execute the Works and to remedy any defects.

7 Time for Completion

7.1
Execution of the Works

The Contractor shall commence the Works on the Commencement Date and shall proceed expeditiously and without delay and shall complete the Works within the Time for Completion.

7.2
Programme

Within the time stated in the Appendix, the Contractor shall submit to the Employer a programme for the Works in the form stated in the Appendix.

7.3
Extension of Time

Subject to Sub-Clause 10.3, the Contractor shall be entitled to an extension to the Time for Completion if he is or will be delayed by any of the Employer's Liabilities.

On receipt of an application from the Contractor, the Employer shall consider all supporting details provided by the Contractor and shall extend the Time for Completion as appropriate.

7.4
Late Completion

If the Contractor fails to complete the Works within the Time for Completion, the Contractor's only liability to the Employer for such failure shall be to pay the amount stated in the Appendix for each day for which he fails to complete the Works.

8 Taking-Over

8.1
Completion

The Contractor may notify the Employer when he considers that the Works are complete.

8.2
Taking-Over Notice

The Employer shall notify the Contractor when he considers that the Contractor has completed the Works stating the date accordingly. Alternatively, the Employer may notify the Contractor that the Works, although not fully complete, are ready for taking over, stating the date accordingly.

The Employer shall take over the Works upon the issue of this notice. The Contractor shall promptly complete any outstanding work and, subject to Clause 9, clear the Site.

9 Remedying Defects

9.1
Remedying Defects

The Employer may at any time prior to the expiry of the period stated in the Appendix, notify the Contractor of any defects or outstanding work. The Contractor shall remedy at no cost to the Employer any defects due to the Contractor's design, Materials, Plant or workmanship not being in accordance with the Contract.

The cost of remedying defects attributable to any other cause shall be valued as a Variation. Failure to remedy any defects or complete outstanding work within a reasonable time of the Employer's notice shall entitle the Employer to carry out all necessary work at the Contractor's cost.

9.2

Uncovering and Testing

The Employer may give instruction as to the uncovering and/or testing of any work. Unless as a result of any uncovering and/or testing it is established that the Contractor's design, Materials, Plant or workmanship are not in accordance with the Contract, the Contractor shall be paid for such uncovering and/or testing as a Variation in accordance with Sub-Clause 10.2.

10 Variations and Claims

10.1
Right to Vary

The Employer may instruct Variations.

10.2

Valuation of Variations

Variations shall be valued as follows:

a) at a lump sum price agreed between the Parties, or
b) where appropriate, at rates in the Contract, or
c) in the absence of appropriate rates, the rates in the Contract shall be used as the basis for valuation, or failing which
d) at appropriate new rates, as may be agreed or which the Employer considers appropriate, or
e) if the Employer so instructs, at daywork rates set out in the Appendix for which the Contractor shall keep records of hours of labour and Contractor's Equipment, and of Materials used.

10.3

Early Warning

A Party shall notify the other as soon as he is aware of any circumstance which may delay or disrupt the Works, or which may give rise to a claim for additional payment. The Contractor shall take all reasonable steps to minimise these effects.

The Contractor's entitlement to extension to the Time for Completion or additional payment shall be limited to the time and payment which would have been due if he had given prompt notice and had taken all reasonable steps.

10.4

Right to Claim

If the Contractor incurs Cost as a result of any of the Employer's Liabilities, the Contractor shall be entitled to the amount of such Cost. If as a result of any of the Employer's Liabilities, it is necessary to change the Works, this shall be dealt with as a Variation.

10.5

Variation and Claim Procedure

The Contractor shall submit to the Employer an itemised make-up of the value of Variations and claims within 28 days of the instruction or of the event giving rise to the claim. The Employer shall check and if possible agree the value. In the absence of agreement, the Employer shall determine the value.

 Short Form of Contract

11 Contract Price and Payment

11.1

Valuation of the Works   The Works shall be valued as provided for in the Appendix, subject to Clause 10.

11.2

Monthly Statements   The Contractor shall be entitled to be paid at monthly intervals:

a)   the value of the Works executed,

b)   the percentage stated in the Appendix of the value of Materials and Plant delivered to the Site at a reasonable time,

subject to any additions or deductions which may be due.

The Contractor shall submit each month to the Employer a statement showing the amounts to which he considers himself entitled.

11.3

Interim Payments   Within 28 days of delivery of each statement, the Employer shall pay to the Contractor the amount shown in the Contractor's statement less retention at the rate stated in the Appendix, and less any amount for which the Employer has specified his reasons for disagreement. The Employer shall not be bound by any sum previously considered by him to be due to the Contractor.

The Employer may withhold interim payments until he receives the performance security under Sub-Clause 4.4 (if any).

11.4

Payment of First Half of Retention   One half of the retention shall be paid by the Employer to the Contractor within 14 days after issuing the notice under Sub-Clause 8.2.

11.5

Payment of Second Half of Retention   The remainder of the retention shall be paid by the Employer to the Contractor within 14 days after either the expiry of the period stated in the Appendix, or the remedying of notified defects or the completion of outstanding work, all as referred to in Sub-Clause 9.1, whichever is the later.

11.6

Final Payment   Within 42 days of the latest of the events listed in Sub-Clause 11.5 above, the Contractor shall submit a final account to the Employer together with any documentation reasonably required to enable the Employer to ascertain the final contract value.

Within 28 days after the submission of this final account, the Employer shall pay to the Contractor any amount due. If the Employer disagrees with any part of the Contractor's final account, he shall specify his reasons for disagreement when making payment.

11.7

Currency   Payment shall be in the currency stated in the Appendix.

11.8

Delayed Payment   The Contractor shall be entitled to interest at the rate stated in the Appendix for each day the Employer fails to pay beyond the prescribed payment period.

AGREEMENT

GENERAL
CONDITIONS

RULES FOR
ADJUDICATION

GUIDANCE

Default 12

12.1
Default by Contractor

If the Contractor abandons the Works, refuses or fails to comply with a valid instruction of the Employer or fails to proceed expeditiously and without delay, or is, despite a written complaint, in breach of the Contract, the Employer may give notice referring to this Sub-Clause and stating the default.

If the Contractor has not taken all practicable steps to remedy the default within 14 days after the Contractor's receipt of the Employer's notice, the Employer may by a second notice given within a further 21 days, terminate the Contract. The Contractor shall then demobilise from the Site leaving behind Materials and Plant and any Contractor's Equipment which the Employer instructs in the second notice is to be used until the completion of the Works.

12.2
Default by Employer

If the Employer fails to pay in accordance with the Contract, or is, despite a written complaint, in breach of the Contract, the Contractor may give notice referring to this Sub-Clause and stating the default. If the default is not remedied within 7 days after the Employer's receipt of this notice, the Contractor may suspend the execution of all or parts of the Works.

If the default is not remedied within 28 days after the Employer's receipt of the Contractor's notice, the Contractor may by a second notice given within a further 21 days, terminate the Contract. The Contractor shall then demobilise from the Site.

12.3
Insolvency

If a Party is declared insolvent under any applicable law, the other Party may by notice terminate the Contract immediately. The Contractor shall then demobilise from the Site leaving behind, in the case of the Contractor's insolvency, any Contractor's Equipment which the Employer instructs in the notice is to be used until the completion of the Works.

12.4
Payment upon Termination

After termination, the Contractor shall be entitled to payment of the unpaid balance of the value of the Works executed and of the Materials and Plant reasonably delivered to the Site, adjusted by the following:

a) any sums to which the Contractor is entitled under Sub-Clause 10.4,
b) any sums to which the Employer is entitled,
c) if the Employer has terminated under Sub-Clause 12.1 or 12.3, the Employer shall be entitled to a sum equivalent to 20% of the value of those parts of the Works not executed at the date of the termination,
d) if the Contractor has terminated under Sub-Clause 12.2 or 12.3, the Contractor shall be entitled to the Cost of his suspension and demobilisation together with a sum equivalent to 10% of the value of those parts of the Works not executed at the date of termination.

The net balance due shall be paid or repaid within 28 days of the notice of termination.

13 Risk and Responsibility

13.1
Contractor's Care of the Works

The Contractor shall take full responsibility for the care of the Works from the Commencement Date until the date of the Employer's notice under Sub-Clause 8.2. Responsibility shall then pass to the Employer. If any loss or damage happens to the Works during the above period, the Contractor shall rectify such loss or damage so that the Works conform with the Contract.

Unless the loss or damage happens as a result of an Employer's Liability, the Contractor shall indemnify the Employer, the Employer's contractors, agents and employees against all loss or damage happening to the Works and against all claims or expense arising out of the Works caused by a breach of the Contract, by negligence or by other default of the Contractor, his agents or employees.

13.2
Force Majeure

If a Party is or will be prevented from performing any of its obligations by Force Majeure, the Party affected shall notify the other Party immediately. If necessary, the Contractor shall suspend the execution of the Works and, to the extent agreed with the Employer, demobilise the Contractor's Equipment.

If the event continues for a period of 84 days, either Party may then give notice of termination which shall take effect 28 days after the giving of the notice.

After termination, the Contractor shall be entitled to payment of the unpaid balance of the value of the Works executed and of the Materials and Plant reasonably delivered to the Site, adjusted by the following:

a)   any sums to which the Contractor is entitled under Sub-Clause 10.4,
b)   the Cost of his suspension and demobilisation,
c)   any sums to which the Employer is entitled.

The net balance due shall be paid or repaid within 28 days of the notice of termination.

14 Insurance

14.1
Extent of Cover

The Contractor shall, prior to commencing the Works, effect and thereafter maintain insurances in the joint names of the Parties:

a)   for loss and damage to the Works, Materials, Plant and the Contractor's Equipment,
b)   for liability of both Parties for loss, damage, death or injury to third parties or their property arising out of the Contractor's performance of the Contract, including the Contractor's liability for damage to the Employer's property other than the Works, and
c)   for liability of both Parties and of any Employer's representative for death or injury to the Contractor's personnel except to the extent that liability arises from the negligence of the Employer, any Employer's representative or their employees.

AGREEMENT

GENERAL
CONDITIONS

RULES FOR
ADJUDICATION

GUIDANCE

| 14.2 | All insurances shall conform with any requirements detailed in the Appendix. The policies shall be issued by insurers and in terms approved by the Employer. The Contractor shall provide the Employer with evidence that any required policy is in force and that the premiums have been paid. |

14.2
Arrangements

All insurances shall conform with any requirements detailed in the Appendix. The policies shall be issued by insurers and in terms approved by the Employer. The Contractor shall provide the Employer with evidence that any required policy is in force and that the premiums have been paid.

All payments received from insurers relating to loss or damage to the Works shall be held jointly by the Parties and used for the repair of the loss or damage or as compensation for loss or damage that is not to be repaired.

14.3

Failure to Insure

If the Contractor fails to effect or keep in force any of the insurances referred to in the previous Sub-Clauses, or fails to provide satisfactory evidence, policies or receipts, the Employer may, without prejudice to any other right or remedy, effect insurance for the cover relevant to such default and pay the premiums due and recover the same as a deduction from any other monies due to the Contractor.

15 Resolution of Disputes

15.1
Adjudication

Unless settled amicably, any dispute or difference which arises between the Contractor and the Employer out of or in connection with the Contract, including any valuation or other decision of the Employer, shall be referred by either Party to adjudication in accordance with the attached Rules for Adjudication ("the Rules"). The adjudicator shall be any person agreed by the Parties. In the event of disagreement, the adjudicator shall be appointed in accordance with the Rules.

15.2

Notice of Dissatisfaction

If a Party is dissatisfied with the decision of the adjudicator or if no decision is given within the time set out in the Rules, the Party may give notice of dissatisfaction referring to this Sub-Clause within 28 days of receipt of the decision or the expiry of the time for the decision. If no notice of dissatisfaction is given within the specified time, the decision shall be final and binding on the Parties. If notice of dissatisfaction is given within the specified time, the decision shall be binding on the Parties who shall give effect to it without delay unless and until the decision of the adjudicator is revised by an arbitrator.

15.3

Arbitration

A dispute which has been the subject of a notice of dissatisfaction shall be finally settled by a single arbitrator under the rules specified in the Appendix. In the absence of agreement, the arbitrator shall be designated by the appointing authority specified in the Appendix. Any hearing shall be held at the place specified in the Appendix and in the language referred to in Sub-Clause 1.5.

INDEX OF SUB-CLAUSES

AGREEMENT

GENERAL CONDITIONS

RULES FOR ADJUDICATION

GUIDANCE

SHORT FORM of Contract

Particular Conditions

First Edition 1999

FEDERATION INTERNATIONALE DES INGENIEURS-CONSEILS
INTERNATIONAL FEDERATION OF CONSULTING ENGINEERS
INTERNATIONALE VEREINIGUNG BERATENDER INGENIEURE
FEDERACION INTERNACIONAL DE INGENIEROS CONSULTORES

Particular Conditions

Note

It is intended that the Short Form of Contract will work satisfactorily without any Particular Conditions. However, if the requirement of the project makes it desirable to amend any Clause or to add provisions to the Contract, the amendments and additions should be set out on pages headed Particular Conditions. Care should be taken with the drafting of such Clauses especially in view of the high priority given to the Particular Conditions by Sub-Clause 1.3.

SHORT FORM of Contract

RULES FOR ADJUDICATION

Rules for Adjudication

First Edition 1999

FEDERATION INTERNATIONALE DES INGENIEURS-CONSEILS
INTERNATIONAL FEDERATION OF CONSULTING ENGINEERS
INTERNATIONALE VEREINIGUNG BERATENDER INGENIEURE
FEDERACION INTERNACIONAL DE INGENIEROS CONSULTORES

FIDIC

AGREEMENT

GENERAL
CONDITIONS

RULES FOR
ADJUDICATION

GUIDANCE

Rules for Adjudication

referred to in Sub-Clause 15.1

General	1	Any reference in the Conditions of Contract to the Rules for Adjudication shall be deemed to be a reference to these Rules.
	2	Definitions in the Contract shall apply in these Rules.
Appointment of Adjudicator	3	The Parties shall jointly ensure the appointment of the Adjudicator. The Adjudicator shall be a suitably qualified person.
	4	If for any reason the appointment of the Adjudicator is not agreed at the latest within 14 days of the reference of a dispute in accordance with these Rules, then either Party may apply, with a copy of the application to the other Party, to any appointing authority named in the Contract or, if none, to the President of FIDIC or his nominee, to appoint an Adjudicator, and such appointment shall be final and conclusive.
	5	The Adjudicator's appointment may be terminated by mutual agreement of the Parties. The Adjudicator's appointment shall expire when the Works have been completed or when any disputes referred to the Adjudicator shall have been withdrawn or decided, whichever is the later.
Terms of Appointment	6	The Adjudicator is to be, and is to remain throughout his appointment, impartial and independent of the Parties and shall immediately disclose in writing to the Parties anything of which he becomes aware which could affect his impartiality or independence.
	7	The Adjudicator shall not give advice to the Parties or their representatives concerning the conduct of the project of which the Works form part other than in accordance with these Rules.
	8	The Adjudicator shall not be called as a witness by the Parties to give evidence concerning any dispute in connection with, or arising out of, the Contract.
	9	The Adjudicator shall treat the details of the Contract and all activities and hearings of the Adjudicator as confidential and shall not disclose the same without the prior written consent of the Parties. The Adjudicator shall not, without the consent of the Parties, assign or delegate any of his work under these Rules or engage legal or technical assistance.
	10	The Adjudicator may resign by giving 28 days' notice to the Parties. In the event of resignation, death or incapacity, termination or a failure or refusal to perform the duties of Adjudicator under these Rules, the Parties shall agree upon a replacement Adjudicator within 14 days or Rule 4 shall apply.

AGREEMENT

GENERAL
CONDITIONS

RULES FOR
ADJUDICATION

GUIDANCE

11   The Adjudicator shall in no circumstances be liable for any claims for anything done or omitted in the discharge of the Adjudicator's duties unless the act or omission is shown to have been in bad faith.

12   If the Adjudicator shall knowingly breach any of the provisions of Rule 6 or act in bad faith, he shall not be entitled to any fees or expenses hereunder and shall reimburse each of the Parties for any fees and expenses properly paid to him if, as a consequence of such breach any proceedings or decisions of the Adjudicator are rendered void or ineffective.

Payment

13   The Adjudicator shall be paid the fees and expenses set out in the Adjudicator's Agreement.

14   The retainer fee, if applicable, shall be payment in full for:

(a)   being available, on 28 days' notice, for all hearings and Site visits;

(b)   all office overhead expenses such as secretarial services, photocopying and office supplies incurred in connection with his duties;

(c)   all services performed hereunder except those performed during the days referred to in Rule 15.

15   The daily fee shall be payable for each working day preparing for or attending Site visits or hearings or preparing decisions including any associated travelling time.

16   The retainer and daily fees shall remain fixed for the period of tenure of the Adjudicator.

17   All payments to the Adjudicator shall be made by the Contractor who will be entitled to be reimbursed half by the Employer. The Contractor shall pay invoices addressed to him within 28 days of receipt. The Adjudicator's invoices for any monthly retainer shall be submitted quarterly in advance and invoices for daily fees and expenses shall be submitted following the conclusion of a Site visit or hearing. All invoices shall contain a brief description of the activities performed during the relevant period. The Adjudicator may suspend work if any invoice remains unpaid at the expiry of the period for payment, provided that 7 days prior notice has been given to both Parties.

18   If the Contractor fails to pay an invoice addressed to it, the Employer shall be entitled to pay the sum due to the Adjudicator and recover the sum paid from the Contractor.

Procedure for Obtaining Adjudicator's Decision

19   A dispute between the Parties may be referred in writing by either Party to the Adjudicator for his decision, with a copy to the other Party. If the Adjudicator has not been agreed or appointed, the dispute shall be referred in writing to the other Party, together with a proposal for the appointment of an Adjudicator. A reference shall identify the dispute and refer to these Rules.

20   The Adjudicator may decide to visit the Site. The Adjudicator may decide to conduct a hearing in which event he shall decide on the date, place and duration for the hearing. The Adjudicator may request that written statements from the Parties be presented to him prior to, at or after the hearing. The Parties shall promptly provide the Adjudicator with sufficient copies of any documentation and information relevant to the Contract that he may request.

© FIDIC 1999   Short Form of Contract

21   The Adjudicator shall act as an impartial expert, not as an arbitrator, and shall have full authority to conduct any hearing as he thinks fit, not being bound by any rules or procedures other than those set out herein. Without limiting the foregoing, the Adjudicator shall have power to:

(a)   decide upon the Adjudicator's own jurisdiction, and as to the scope of any dispute referred to him,

(b)   make use of his own specialist knowledge, if any,

(c)   adopt an inquisitorial procedure,

(d)   decide upon the payment of interest in accordance with the Contract,

(e)   open up, review and revise any opinion, instruction, determination, certificate or valuation, related to the dispute,

(f)   refuse admission to hearings to any persons other than the Employer, the Contractor and their respective representatives, and to proceed in the absence of any Party who the Adjudicator is satisfied received notice of the hearing.

22   All communications between either of the Parties and the Adjudicator and all hearings shall be in the language of the Adjudicator's Agreement. All such communications shall be copied to the other Party.

23   No later than the fifty-sixth day after the day on which the Adjudicator received a reference or, if later, the day on which the Adjudicator's Agreement came into effect, the Adjudicator shall give written notice of his decision to the Parties. Such decision shall include reasons and state that it is given under these Rules.

AGREEMENT

GENERAL
CONDITIONS

RULES FOR
ADJUDICATION

GUIDANCE

Adjudicator's Agreement

Identification of Project:

_____

(the "Project")

Name and address of the Employer:

_____

(the "Employer")

Name and address of Contractor:

_____

(the "Contractor")

Name and address of Adjudicator:

_____

(the "Adjudicator")

Whereas the Employer and the Contractor have entered into a contract ("the Contract") for the execution of the Project and wish to appoint the Adjudicator to act as adjudicator in accordance with the Rules for Adjudication ["the Rules"].

The Employer, Contractor and Adjudicator agree as follows:

1.   The Rules and the dispute provisions of the Contract shall form part of this Agreement.

2.   The Adjudicator shall be paid:

    A retainer fee of _____ per calendar month (where applicable)

    A daily fee of _____

    Expenses (including the cost of telephone calls, courier charges, faxes and telexes incurred in connection with his duties; all reasonable and necessary travel expenses, hotel accommodation and subsistence and other direct travel expenses).

    Receipts will be required for all expenses.

AGREEMENT

GENERAL
CONDITIONS

RULES FOR
ADJUDICATION

GUIDANCE

3.   The Adjudicator agrees to act as adjudicator in accordance with the Rules and has disclosed to the Parties any previous or existing relationship with the Parties or others concerned with the Project.

4.   This Agreement shall be governed by the law of _____

5.   The language of this Agreement shall be _____

SIGNED BY _____

for and on behalf of the Employer in the presence of

Witness _____
Name _____
Address _____
Date _____

SIGNED BY _____

for and on behalf of the Contractor in the presence of

Witness _____
Name _____
Address _____
Date _____

SIGNED BY _____

for and on behalf of the Adjudicator in the presence of

Witness _____
Name _____
Address _____
Date _____

AGREEMENT

GENERAL CONDITIONS

PARTICULAR CONDITIONS

RULES FOR ADJUDICATION

NOTES FOR GUIDANCE

SHORT FORM of Contract

Notes for Guidance

First Edition 1999

FEDERATION INTERNATIONALE DES INGENIEURS-CONSEILS
INTERNATIONAL FEDERATION OF CONSULTING ENGINEERS
INTERNATIONALE VEREINIGUNG BERATENDER INGENIEURE
FEDERACION INTERNACIONAL DE INGENIEROS CONSULTORES

FIDIC

AGREEMENT

GENERAL
CONDITIONS

RULES FOR
ADJUDICATION

GUIDANCE

Notes for Guidance

(not forming part of the Contract)

General

The objective of this Contract is to express in clear and simple terms traditional procurement concepts. The Contract is intended to be suitable for works of simple content and short duration. If it is required that the Contractor should undertake design, this is also provided for.

There are no Particular Conditions, although these Notes contain alternative wording for consideration in particular circumstances. All necessary additional information is intended to be provided in the Appendix.

A single document is proposed for the form of tender and the agreement. This reflects the simple projects envisaged.

One result of the simple form of Contract is that there is an increased burden on the Employer to set out in the Specification and Drawings the full scope of works, including the extent of any design to be done by the Contractor.

There is no Engineer or Employer's Representative in the formal sense used in some other FIDIC Conditions. The Employer takes all necessary actions. However, the Employer must nominate his authorised spokesman and, if he wishes to engage a consultant to administer the Contract, may appoint a representative with specific delegated duties and authority. The Contractor also nominates a representative.

The Conditions contain no overall limit on the Contractor's liability. If such a limit is required, a Clause should be inserted in the Particular Conditions.

Agreement

The printed form envisages a simple procedure of offer and acceptance. In order to avoid the traps and uncertainties that surround "letters of acceptance" and "letters of intent", it was thought preferable to promote a clear and unambiguous practice.

It is intended that the Employer will write in the Employer's name in the Agreement and fill in the Appendix where appropriate and send two copies to tenderers together with the Specification, Drawings etc forming the tender package. In respect of both copies, the Contractor is to complete, sign and date the Offer section and complete any remaining spaces in the Appendix. Having decided which tender to accept, the Employer signs the Acceptance section of both copies and returns one copy to the Contractor. The Contract comes into effect upon receipt by the Contractor of his copy.

If post-tender negotiations are permitted and changes in specification or price are agreed, then the form can still be used after the Parties have made and initialled the appropriate changes to their respective documents. The Contractor thus makes a revised offer in response to the Employer's revised tender documents and the revised offer is accepted by the Employer signing and returning the Acceptance form. If the changes are extensive, a new form of Agreement should be completed by the Parties.

AGREEMENT

GENERAL
CONDITIONS

RULES FOR
ADJUDICATION

GUIDANCE

As the Contract comes into effect upon receipt of the signed Acceptance by the Contractor, the Employer should take steps to establish when receipt occurs, for example by requiring the Contractor to collect and sign for the Agreement.

When the applicable law imposes any form of tax such as VAT on the Works, the Employer should make clear whether tenderers should include such taxes in their prices. Similarly, if payment is to be made in whole or in part in a currency other than the currency of the Country, the Employer should make this clear to tenderers. See Sub-Clause 11.7.

Appendix

Any Notes for Guidance on the completion of the Appendix are to be found in the Notes to the Clauses concerned. The Employer should complete the Appendix as indicated prior to inviting tenders. Tenderers may be asked to insert a Time for Completion at 1.1.9 if none is specified. Where tenderers are required to submit design with their tenders, the documents containing the tendered design should be identified by the tenderer against item 1.1.1(f) of the Appendix.

A number of suggestions have been made in the Appendix, such as the time for submission of the Contractor's programme under Sub-Clause 7.2 and the amount of retention under Sub-Clause 11.3. If these suggestions are adopted by the Employer, no action is required. Otherwise, they should be deleted and replaced.

General Provisions

1.1   **Definitions**. The definitions in these Conditions are not all the same as those to be found in other FIDIC Contracts. This is as a result of the need for simplicity in Conditions of this sort. Significantly different definitions include Commencement Date, Site, Variation and Works.

1.1.1   "**Contract**". The list of documents serves two purposes: firstly, to identify which documents form part of the Contract; and secondly, to provide an order of priority in the event of conflict between them.

Document identification is necessary to avoid any possible doubt, for example because specifications have been subject to revisions. A complete list of Drawings is always desirable and could be attached on a separate sheet.

There is no need for Particular Conditions but if amendments to these Conditions are required, they should be inserted on the sheet headed Particular Conditions and given priority over the General Conditions. If none, delete the reference.

The Specification should set out in clear terms any design that the Contractor is required to undertake, including the extent to which any design proposals are to be submitted with the tender. If none, the reference to the Contractor's tendered design should be deleted.

If there is no bill of quantities, delete the reference.

If there are additional documents which are required to form part of the Contract, such as schedules of information provided by the Contractor, these should be added by the Employer. Consideration should be given in each case to the required priority.

If a letter of acceptance is used, it should be given high priority, with or in place of the Agreement, for example.

AGREEMENT

GENERAL
CONDITIONS

RULES FOR
ADJUDICATION

GUIDANCE

1.1.7   "**Commencement Date**". The starting date for the Contract is 14 days after the date when the Contractor receives the Agreement signed by the Employer, unless the Parties agree otherwise.

1.1.14   "**Force Majeure**" may include, but is not limited to, exceptional events or circumstances of the kind listed below, so long as all of the four conditions stated in the definition have been satisfied:

     a)   war, hostilities (whether war be declared or not), invasion, act of foreign enemies,

     b)   rebellion, terrorism, revolution, insurrection, military or usurped power, or civil war,

     c)   riot, commotion, disorder, strike or lockout by persons other than the Contractor's personnel and other employees,

     d)   munitions of war, explosive materials, ionising radiation or contamination by radioactivity, except as may be attributable to the Contractor's use of such munitions, explosives, radiation or radio-activity, and

     e)   natural catastrophes such as earthquake, hurricane, typhoon or volcanic activity.

1.1.19   "**Works**". The term "Works" is intended to cover all the obligations of the Contractor, including any design and the remedying of defects.

1.5   **Communications**. The problem of languages is addressed by requiring the important communications such as notices and instructions to be in the language stated in the Appendix. Otherwise there is no "Ruling Language". Any arbitration will be conducted in the specified language.

1.6   Changes to the law after the date of the Contractor's offer are at the Employer's risk and any delay or additional cost are recoverable by the Contractor. If the law of the Contract is not the law of the Country, then Sub-Clause 6.1 should be changed in the Particular Conditions.

The Employer   2.1   Unless the Parties have agreed otherwise, the Site must be handed over by the Employer to the Contractor on the Commencement Date. This is 14 days after the Contract has come into effect, which occurs when the signed Agreement has been returned by the Employer to the Contractor (see also Sub-Clause 1.1.7 above).

2.2   If for any reason, permits etc may also be required from places other than the Country, this Sub-Clause could be limited by the addition at the end of the words:

     "... in the Country but not elsewhere."

2.4   The term "**approval**" is only used in the Conditions in relation to the performance security at Sub-Clause 4.4 and insurances at Sub-Clause 14.1. It is important that risks such as those of poor workmanship or Contractor's design are not transferred to the Employer unintentionally. The Sub-Clause is intended to prevent argument.

Employer's Representatives   3   Two principles guided the drafting of this Clause. Firstly, the Contractor should know who in an Employer organisation is authorised to speak and act for the Employer at any given time. This is achieved by Sub-Clause 3.1: the authorised individual should be named in the Appendix.

Secondly, those Employers who require professional assistance should not be discouraged from doing so and their consultant should have clearly established delegated powers. This is the object of Sub-Clause 3.2. Once appointed, the Employer's representative acts for and in the interests of the Employer. There is no dual role or duty to be impartial. If an impartial Employer's Representative is required with a role similar to the traditional Engineer, then the following words could be used in the Particular Conditions:

> "Replace the final sentence of Sub-Clause 3.2 with the following: "*The Employer's Representative shall exercise in a fair and impartial manner the powers of the Employer under or in connection with the following Sub-Clauses: 1.3, 2.3, 4.2, 4.3, 5.1, 7.3, 8.2, 9.1, 9.2, 10.1, 10.2, 10.5, 11.1 to 11.6, 11.8, 12.1, 13.2 and 14.1.*"

To the extent that the Employer has delegated powers to an Employer's representative, he should be careful not to exercise such powers himself in order to avoid the risk of conflicting instructions, decisions etc.

The Contractor	4.1	Most contracts do not specify the exact standard required for each element of the Works, so some benchmark standard is needed with which the Contractor is to comply. If a more specific set of standards could be referred to for a particular project, then an amendment in the Particular Conditions would be desirable.
	4.4	**Performance Security**. Suggested forms of performance bond (surety bond) or bank guarantee have not been provided. If it is felt that the scale of project warrants security by means of a bond, then local commercial practice should dictate the form. Example forms are included with FIDIC's Conditions of Contract for Construction. The amount and a reference to the desired form of any required security should be set out in the Appendix.
Design by Contractor	5.1	As with all design-build contracts it is essential that the Employer's requirements are set out clearly and precisely. The Appendix should indicate to tenderers the Sub-Clause(s) in the Specification that set out the design requirement. Where the Employer procures any part of the design, the responsibility for design will be shared as this Contract makes the Contractor responsible only for design prepared by him. The extent of the Contractor's design obligation should therefore be clearly stated if disputes are to be avoided. The Conditions avoid the confusing concept of approval of design. Designs are submitted and may be returned with comments or rejected. The Employer need not react at all.
	5.2	The Contractor's responsibility for his design remains, as is made clear here and in Sub-Clause 2.4. In the event of conflict between the Specification and Drawings and the Contractor's tendered design, the order of priority in the Appendix makes it clear that the Employer's documents prevail. This means that if the Employer prefers the Contractor's tendered solution, the Specification and Drawings should be amended before the Contract is signed by the Parties.

The Contractor will have an absolute obligation to ensure that the parts of the Works designed by him are fit for their purpose, provided that the intended purposes are defined in the Contract. The Employer must therefore make clear in the parts of the Specification that impose design obligations, the intended purposes of the part of the Works to be designed by the Contractor. This should be done even where this seems obvious in order to avoid argument about whether an intended purpose is defined or not.

If a party wishes to protect the intellectual property in his design, provision must be made in the Particular Conditions.

Employer's Liabilities 6.1 This Sub-Clause gathers together in one place the grounds for extension of time under Sub-Clause 7.3 and the grounds for claims under Sub-Clause 10.4. There is no time or claim for bad weather although this could be adjusted in the Particular Conditions if so required.

Time for Completion 7.2 The Appendix should stipulate any particular requirements as to the form and level of detail of programme to be submitted. Where Contractor's design is required, the Appendix could stipulate that the programme should show the dates on which it is intended to prepare and submit drawings etc.

7.3 The test for entitlement to an extension of time is whether it is appropriate. This means that if an event under Sub-Clause 6.1 caused critical delay to the Works and it is fair and reasonable to grant an extension of time, the Employer should do so. An extension of time should not be granted to the extent that any failure by the Contractor to give an early warning notice under Sub-Clause 10.3 contributed to the delay.

7.4 There is a maximum amount which the Contractor is liable to pay for late completion specified in the Appendix. 10% of the sum stated in the Agreement is suggested.

Taking-Over 8.2 In line with normal practice, it is not envisaged that the Works need be 100% complete before the Employer may take over. Once the Works are ready to be used for their intended purpose, the notice should be given. There is no provision for taking-over of only parts of the Works but if this is required, provision should be made in the Particular Conditions.

If any tests are required to be completed prior to taking-over, these should be specified in the Specification. The definition of Works is broad enough to include any such tests.

Remedying Defects 9.1 There is no defined Defects Liability Period but during the period - normally 12 months - from the date of taking-over, the Employer may notify the Contractor of defects. The Contractor must remedy such defects within a reasonable time. If he fails to do so, the Employer may employ others for that purpose at the Contractor's cost. The Employer may also notify defects at any time prior to taking-over.

The liability of the Contractor for defects will not normally end with the expiry of the period stated in the Appendix. Although he is then no longer obliged to return to Site to remedy defects, the defect represents a breach of contract for which the Contractor is liable in damages. This liability remains for as long as the law of the Contract stipulates, often 3, 6 or 10 years from the date of the breach. If this long-term liability is to be reduced or eliminated, a Clause in the Particular Conditions is required.

Variations and Claims	10.1	Variation is defined to include any change to the Specification or Drawings included in the Contract. If the Employer requires a change to part of the Works designed by the Contractor either as part of his tender or after the Contract was awarded, then this is to be done by way of an addition to the Specification or Drawings which by Sub-Clause 5.2 will prevail over Contractor's design.

10.2   This Sub-Clause sets out alternative procedures for the valuation of Variations, to be applied in the order of priority given. It applies equally to omissions as to additional works.

       a)   A lump sum should be the first method to be considered as it can encompass the true cost of a Variation and avoid subsequent dispute over the indirect effect. The Employer can invite the Contractor to submit an itemised make-up (Sub-Clause 10.5) before instructing the Variation so that an agreed lump sum can form part of the instruction.

       b)   Alternatively, a more traditional approach can be taken by valuing the Variation at rates in the bill of quantities and any schedules, or

       c)   using these rates as a basis, or

       d)   using new rates.

       e)   Daywork rates are normally used when the Variation is of an indeterminate nature or is out of sequence with the remaining Works. To ensure reasonable daywork rates, provision should be made for these to be priced competitively in the tender documents.

10.3   This Sub-Clause and Sub-Clause 10.5 require the Contractor to notify the Employer of events promptly and to detail any claim within 28 days. If the effects of the event are increased or if the ability of the Employer to verify any claim is affected by the failure to notify, then the Employer is protected.

Contract Price and Payment	11.1	Normally only one of the options in the Appendix should be used to indicate how the sum in the offer is be calculated and presented. The following explains what is intended:

Lump sum price	A lump sum offer without any supporting details. This would be used for very minor works where Variations are not anticipated and the Works will be completed in a short period requiring only one payment to the Contractor.
Lump sum price with schedule of rates	A lump sum offer supported by schedules of rates prepared by the tenderer. This would be a larger contract where Variations and stage payments would be required. If the Employer does not have the resources to prepare his own bill of quantities then this alternative would be suitable.

AGREEMENT

GENERAL
CONDITIONS

RULES FOR
ADJUDICATION

GUIDANCE

Lump sum price with bill of quantities	A lump sum offer based on bill of quantities prepared by the Employer. This would be the same as last but where the Employer has the resources to prepare his own bill of quantities. A better contract would result with an Employer's bill of quantities.
Remeasurement with bill of quantities	A sum subject to remeasurement at the rates offered by the tenderer in the bill of quantities prepared by the Employer. This would be the same as last but would suit a contract where many changes are envisaged to the Works after the Contract has been awarded.
Cost reimbursable	An estimate prepared by the tenderer which will be replaced by the actual cost of the Works calculated in accordance with the terms set by the Employer. This would suit a project where the extent of work cannot be ascertained before the Contract is placed. An example of this would be an emergency reconstruction of a building damaged by fire.

However, if for some special reason, more than one option is selected, for example there is a remeasureable element in a lump sum Contract, then the details should be carefully defined.

The Foreword indicates that this Short Form of Contract is intended for works of short duration. In the event of a contract for works of long duration, a new clause could be inserted at Sub-Clause 11.1 to adjust for the rise and fall in the cost of labour, materials and other imports to the Works. Such a clause could be adapted from the other FIDIC Conditions of Contract.

11.2   If the Contract is for a lump sum, consideration should be given as to how the work is to be valued for the purposes of interim payments. In completing the Appendix for Sub-Clause 11.1, the Employer may request tenderers to submit a cash flow forecast linked to a stage payment proposal for agreement. This would be reviewed in the event of an extension of time made in accordance with Sub-Clause 7.3.

Alternatively, interim payment can be based on valuation of the Works which would also be appropriate for remeasurement and cost reimbursable Contracts. Payment could also be based on the achievement of milestones or a schedule of activities to which values are assigned.

If local law or practice so dictates, an invoice may also be required, in which case it could be submitted with the statement.

11.3   No provision is made for advance payments. If such a payment is to be made, there should be provision in the Particular Conditions and for any security to be provided by the Contractor. An example form of advance payment guarantee is to be found in FIDIC's Conditions of Contract for Construction.

11.4   The deduction of retention is sometimes replaced by the provision of security by the Contractor to the Employer. Alternatively, the entire retention sum deducted is released after taking-over upon the provision by the Contractor of security. In either event, suitable text would be required in the Particular Conditions. An example form of retention guarantee is to be found in FIDIC's Conditions of Contract for Construction.

11.5 The release of the second part of the retention will serve as confirmation that all notified defects have been remedied.

11.7 It is assumed that payments will be in a single currency. If this is not the case, the proportions of different currencies should be stated in the Appendix and provision made in the Specification or the Particular Conditions as to how payment is to be made.

Default

12.1 The Employer may terminate the Contract if the defaulting Contractor does not respond to a formal notice by taking all practicable steps to put right his default. This recognises that not all defaults are capable of correction in 14 days. If termination takes place, the Employer may take over and use the Contractor's Equipment to complete the Works. Care should be taken, however, if the equipment on Site is hired: no specific provision is made to cover this situation and the Employer is unlikely to be able to retain such equipment.

12.2 This provision provides the Contractor's main remedy for non-payment. 7 days after the Employer's receipt of a default notice, which must refer to Sub-Clause 12.2, the Contractor may suspend all or part of his work. 21 days later the option to terminate arises if the Employer persists with non-payment or other default. The Contractor must use his right to terminate within 21 days or lose it. This is to prevent a party abusing a right to terminate in his dealings with the other party for the remainder of the project.

If Contractor's Equipment is essential for the safety or stability of the Works, the Employer will be obliged to agree terms with the Contractor for the retention of such equipment. Local law will often protect the Employer from the immediate and reckless removal of essential items.

12.3 The right of the Employer to retain the Contractor's Equipment may clash with the right of a liquidator or receiver to realise the assets of an insolvent Contractor. Reference to the applicable law would be necessary.

12.4 This Sub-Clause enables the financial aspects of the Contract to be resolved quickly and without the necessity to await the completion of the Works by others. By specifying the damages payable to the innocent party for the defaults leading to the termination, much delay, complication and scope for dispute are avoided. The Employer's costs in obtaining a replacement contractor will generally be higher than the Contractor's loss of profit.

Risk and Responsibility

13.1 Although the Contractor is responsible for the Works prior to taking-over, he is protected by the obligation to insure the Works under Clause 14 and by his ability to recover under Clause 6 his Cost if one of the Employer's Liabilities occurs.

13.2 To qualify as Force Majeure, events must prevent performance of an obligation. See also the definition at Sub-Clause 1.1.14. Notice must be given at once.

 Short Form of Contract

Insurance	14.1	The Employer should set out his precise requirements in the Appendix. Third Party, public liability insurance would normally be mandatory. As smaller contracts are likely to fall within tenderers' standing Contractors' All Risk (CAR) insurance policies, tenderers should generally be asked to submit details of their insurance cover with their tenders.

Any requirements for insurance after the date of the Employer's notice under Sub-Clause 8.2, or arising from taking-over parts of the Works, should be covered by Particular Conditions. See also Clause 13.

If the Employer wishes to take out the insurances instead of the Contractor, the following should be used as a Particular Condition in place of Sub-Clause 14.1:

"Replace the text of Sub-Clause 14.1 with the following: "*The Employer shall, prior to the Commencement Date, effect insurance in the joint names of the Parties of the types, in the amounts and with the exclusions stipulated in the Appendix. The Employer shall provide the Contractor with evidence that any required policy is in force and that the premiums have been paid.*"

Sub-Clauses 14.2 and 14.3 should be deleted if the Employer takes out the insurances.

It should be noted that in the event of the Employer's failure to insure, the Contractor may give notice under Sub-Clause 12.2.

Resolution of Disputes	15.1	There are advantages in appointing an adjudicator from the outset even though the adjudicator may not be required to take any action or earn any fee unless and until a dispute is referred to him. Delays will inevitably occur if the parties initiate the procedure to appoint an adjudicator only when a dispute has arisen. It is therefore recommended that the Employer propose a person to act as adjudicator either at tender stage or shortly after the Agreement is signed and that the matter is discussed and agreed as soon as possible.

Care should be taken about whether an adjudicator should be local or from a neutral country. Although the adjudicator should be impartial, the costs of employing someone from a third country could be disproportionate if it is necessary for the adjudicator to visit or if a hearing became necessary. However, in view of the costs involved in arbitration, even of minor disputes, any extra cost of a truly impartial adjudicator is a recommended investment.

It is intended that all decisions made by the Employer or his representative should be capable of being reviewed by an adjudicator and, if required, by an arbitrator.

	15.3	Arbitration may not be commenced unless the dispute has first been the subject of an adjudication. The Rules of arbitration should be stipulated in the Appendix. The UNCITRAL Rules are recommended. However, if administered arbitration is required, that is arbitration overseen and administered by an arbitral institution, the ICC Rules could be specified. The ICC Court of Arbitration and its Secretariat in Paris appoints and replaces arbitrators, checks the form of terms of reference and awards and generally monitors progress and the performance of arbitrators. Where alternative

AGREEMENT

GENERAL
CONDITIONS

RULES FOR
ADJUDICATION

GUIDANCE

arbitration rules are chosen that include a procedure for the appointment of an arbitrator, the authority designated in the Appendix to make the appointment should be changed to reflect this. For example, if ICC Rules are chosen, then the appointing authority should normally be changed to "ICC Court of Arbitration". The place of arbitration is significant as the arbitration law of the place of arbitration will apply in such matters as the ability of a party to appeal.